GREG'S Gift

An End-of-Life Planning Guide to
Help You Leave a Legacy for Your Loved Ones

KATHY GOLASZEWSKI

Praise for Greg's Gift

"As an attorney, I highly recommend *Greg's Gift* because it is an extraordinarily useful book for those who survive the passing of a loved one, and it has all the information any attorney needs to handle a loved ones' estate. More importantly, *Greg's Gift* is a lasting reminder of just how much you care for the loved ones you leave behind. Greg passed away shortly after his daughter's wedding and there's no doubt in my mind that he willed himself to live longer than God had planned just so he could be there for his daughter and his family on that special day. I learned from Greg about what it truly means to be a loving spouse and father. So, it was no surprise to learn that Greg had left Kathy his gift."

~ David S. Desmond, Esq.

"This book is, in a way, a successor to the making of a bucket list. This book contains things that our loved ones need to know after we are gone, to make their lives easier and less stressful. Thanks to Kathy, for your gift as well, for offering this up to all, and allowing those of us who knew him to keep Greg in our memories."

~ Harvey Kornbluth

"During my career I've taken care of very ill patients, but I never thought about the financial and legal responsibilities of the surviving family members when their loved one passes. Nor did I think about what this would mean for me personally when or if I were in the same situation. However, now that I'm retired and facing end of life issues, I find *Greg's Gift* the perfect guide to organize and record all important documents, deeds, certificates, insurances, stocks, etc., that are necessary for relatives to be aware of before it is too late. Great advice!"

~ Jacqueline Siller, RN

This book is dedicated to my late husband, Greg, who was extremely thoughtful and loving to leave me with this "how to" book. A special thank you to my beautiful daughter, Mary, and my wonderful son, Jimmy, who have kept me going with their love, patience, and humor.

Table of Contents

Introduction

HOW THIS BOOK CAME ABOUT

Greg Golaszewski was born on November 7, 1956. We first met in 1977 at a Macy's department store where we both were working. We started dating and were married on November 21, 1982. He was my best friend. We have a daughter, who was born in 1994, and a son born in 1997. Greg was a wonderful father; fun, loving, smart and caring. He was Vice President of Finance in his company, working in corporate tax in the financial business sector. He volunteered at our church with the summer festival fundraiser, the "Breakfast with Santa" annual event, and covered lunch duty once in a while! He coached soccer, basketball, and baseball. He was a member of the Knights of Columbus and loved volunteering at the senior bingo night.

Greg was diagnosed with stage 4 prostate cancer in the latter part of 2014. He was devastated that his future plans would be cut short and that he would no longer have a presence in our children's lives and in my life. We had so many dreams and plans for the future. Our world, as we knew it, would be changed forever.

Greg had always taken care of the finances and household expenses, and this is why he started to write this "end-of-life" planning book for me. It was to help me take on these new responsibilities once he passed on. Greg personalized his book to me. He wrote as if he were speaking to me: "Press *agree* to terms and conditions, Kathy. It is o.k. to press *agree!*" I still hear his humor and sincerity when I read his words. In his book he covered household responsibilities as well as bills to pay, homeowners insurance, car insurance, COBRA, car maintenance, and college tuition, to name a few.

This book was not easy for Greg knowing he was not going to be here for long, but it was with so much love for our family and for me that he did this.

Greg passed away on May 17, 2018. I was and am still devastated by his loss and living without him. However, *Greg's Gift* helps me find the strength and courage to move forward. I know this book is not only a guide for me but part of his legacy that I am now passing on to others. With this said, if you fill out this book as you do your bills and update items as they change, you too can leave a legacy to your loved ones. It may be a bit tedious and difficult, depending on each one's circumstances. However, the rewards are tremendous, and your loved ones will appreciate it forever.

Since Greg's passing, I've met many people who lost their loved ones. When I mention that Greg left me a book, they all have said they wished they had something like this to help guide them in the aftermath. This book may seem like a lot of work at first, but once you get started and keep updating it, you will feel more organized and comfortable knowing that if anything happens to you, your loved ones will know how much you care.

This "Gift" is not a death sentence but a legacy of love. I attribute my being able to deal with the huge loss of my husband not physically being here with the closeness of this book. I truly feel his presence close to me, watching over me and pointing me in the right direction.

I hope you accept this "Gift," fill it out for your loved ones, and personalize it as you see fit. Even if you live alone, this book will help you keep a record of where your important papers are.

At the beginning of most chapters, I will share some personal stories of mine. I hope you will be encouraged to take the time and fill in this book with your memorable stories. At the end of each chapter, you will find a page to add your story. It can be a memory, an important detail, or a humorous thought that you could pass forward as part of your legacy. Take all the time you need to create this beautiful gift and pass it forward! I hope you feel the sense of fulfillment and love with your "Gift" as you pass this treasure on. A beautiful friend of mine offered this advice: "Too soon we get old, and too late we get smart!" Please don't wait too long to get started on this book!

Like the poem that follows, I believe this "Gift" will allow me to share a part of my husband Greg with all of you:

Give What's Left of Me Away

Now that I'm gone,
Remember me with a smile and laughter,
And Cry if you need to cry,
Cry with your brother or sister
Who walks in grief beside you.

And when you need me,
Put your arms around anyone
And give to them
What you need to give to me.

There are so many
Who need so much.
I want to leave you something.
Something much better
Than words or sounds.

Look for me
In the people
I've known and loved and helped
in some special way.
Let me live in your heart
As well as your mind.

You can love me most
By letting your love
Reach out to our loved ones.
By embracing them
And living in their love.

Love does not die,
People do.
So, when all that's left of me is love,
Give me away as best as you can
-Author Unknown

Disclaimer:

The information in this book applies to most people. Each state or county may have additional or slightly different applications or rules; however, the basic "to-do list" is just that, basic. Some states may require different registrations, and bills may not be payable in 6-month intervals. Each state may have particulars, but this book is a guideline, and a tool to share your precious treasures and legacy with loved ones as well as help you through the trail of passwords and online information. Besides the disclaimers of each particular state with regards to cars, insurance, taxes, and bill pay, and even the encouragement to seek financial advice, this book touches on our everyday responsibilities and obligations. It is not a textbook or a guide for finances, etc. This author disclaims any responsibility or misunderstanding, which incurred as a consequence of the contents of this book. The author makes no claims or promises or guarantees about accuracy, completeness and disclaims liability for errors or omissions.

Chapter 1

PERSONAL FINANCES

Greg worked in finance, and he felt comfortable doing online banking. However, I was a person who never used an ATM. I know that may sound foreign to some of you, but I am one of those people who go to the teller. I do, however, use a credit card! My husband would go to the ATM and get me cash if I needed it. Greg spoiled me, and I knew it! By the way, I had never pumped gas either!

Greg paid a lot of our bills online and had some bill payments deducted from our checking account. In his "end-of-life" planning book, Greg documented each bill we paid throughout the year. Some bills he indicated are paid monthly, quarterly, semi-annually, yearly, and seasonally. Some are automatic deductions, and some he paid by manually logging onto the website. He set up our banking online and documented each password as well as which bills he paid by autopay.

Some of us still go up to bank tellers and write checks to pay our bills. The next generation is doing everything online. They take pictures from their phones to deposit a check, and they transfer money from one account to another via their phone. It is so important for you and your loved ones to document how bills are paid to prevent the risk of bills not being paid on time.

Now It's Your Turn:

Online Banking:

Go to the website of your Bank.

Click on "online banking."

If your spouse or loved one left you the username and password that's a great help. If not, create your own login and password. You will need your banking account number.

Be aware that it is not legal to access these accounts without going through the proper channels. It may be just showing a birth certificate or going through probate and the appropriate channels. This step is easiest if it is a joint account, and if you have a documented beneficiary. However, by writing this information here, your loved ones will know what types of accounts you have and where you bank.

Technically you can only use your spouse's login if you had a joint account, otherwise the bank would need a death certificate. And if no beneficiary, the estate will have to be probated to see where and whom the money should go to. You will need a death certificate and proof of identification either way.

Record them in this book.

Click on LOGIN and use the username and password.

Bank: _____

Username: _____

Password: _____

If you forget your password or need to change them, update the new ones here. This may change multiple times so always be sure to update with the correct password.

Username: _____

Password: _____

If you are now creating a new login, write the bank name here:

Bank: _____

Username: _____

Password: _____

(Space for changes)

Username: _____

Password: _____

If you have more than one Bank, list them here:

Bank Name: _____

Type of account: _____
(Checking, money market, savings etc.)

Account number: _____

Username: _____

Password: _____

Bank: _____

Type of account: _____

Account number:_____

Username:_____

Password: _____

**Document any automatic debits or charges from this bank in this book, i.e., any automatic payments that you have set up. Automatic payments can be paying the full amount or a specific amount of your bill or credit card. By setting this up, you could prevent missing a payment. Be sure to note which payments are automatically deducted to ensure you have enough money in your account to cover these monthly payments.

If you opt not to use a credit card, you can pay bills directly from your checking account. These bill payments may be set up to notify you through your email address. Be sure to update any changes in your email addresses if the time comes.

Automatic checking account debits to keep track of (examples listed below):

Phone Bill: _____

Home: _____

Cell: _____

Electric: _____

TV: _____

Oil: _____

Gas: _____

Tuition: _____

Church: _____

Insurance: _____

Some car insurance is paid every month for six months of the year and homeowner's insurance can also be paid six months of the year. This needs to be budgeted into your billing schedule.

Health insurance: _____

Some companies allow credit cards, but most prefer debit from a checking account. Be sure to check with your health insurance provider for payment methods.

Prescription medications: _____

_____

_____

B. CD's (Certificates of Deposit)

Bank with CD: _____

Date it is due:_____

Bank with CD: _____

Date it is due: _____

Bank with CD: _____

Date it is due: _____

C. Safe Deposit Box:

Name and Location of box: _____

Box Number: _____

Location of keys: _____

Person who can access: _____

List all the important items kept in your safe deposit box.

1. _____

2. _____

3. _____

4. _____

5. _____

6. _____

7. _____

**You may want to also keep a video or pictures of your home in your safe deposit box, in the event of a fire. That way, you have proof for your insurance company.

Your Story

This is your time to share your thoughts and stories for your family.

Chapter 2

CREDIT CARD DETAILS

It was so overwhelming to take on the task of paying the bills. Greg had been the one in the family to handle the finances, and now I found myself with this new and permanent role and responsibility. I found this very difficult. Greg had told me he needed to pay off a bill in May. He passed away before he was able to. I had known about this bill, and I planned to do it in June. But, I couldn't push the submit button on the computer. It was traumatic. So, I incurred a late charge from this credit card company. I called the credit card company based on a friend's recommendation that I should fight the late charge. The customer service representative on the phone said that Greg had a 99 cents monthly charge for the iCloud. He asked me if I wanted to cancel it since my husband was not using it. I was torn. Near the end of his life, Greg told me "Don't change anything for six months. Learn the bills, but don't change anything for six months." Even though Greg had told me not to change anything for six months, I didn't want to incur a late fee, and therefore I discontinued it.

That was on a Friday.

I woke up on Saturday morning, and I realized that by canceling the iCloud I had given up Greg's pictures! Did I lose everything? And, he told me not to change anything! I was devastated.

I immediately called Apple. They told me to upload his pictures to my computer, which I had no clue how to do. They sent me emails on how to do it. This was very difficult since I was not comfortable with the computer. I spent the entire weekend figuring out how to airdrop and upload pictures. It was very stressful. I again called Apple on Sunday for their help, and they recommended that I go through Greg's emails and notes. I felt overwhelmed by the task because I personally have over 500 emails and certainly a lot more notes. And now I had to go through Greg's. I took a deep breath and I started. Greg had about 300 emails and a few notes with many about pain medications and schedules or whom he needed to return calls to. While going through his notes, I found a note he wrote to our daughter and son in October of 2017. This is the note I will leave you with at the end of this book. How emotional I was to have found this amazing "gift"! All because I didn't remember NOT to do anything for six months! And, to top this, I again called Apple Support, and the man on the phone recommended I put Greg's account on my credit card until I was ready to stop. How easy was that? Then, he offered to help transfer all Greg's pictures to my computer. After accepting his connection to my computer, he said, "You might want to charge this once in a while, Kathy."

It was a serendipitous moment since, on the 16th of May, Greg had asked me for his phone. He always had it with him to call or text me or to see the time. I had moved it for a few moments while I did his care, but he was afraid I would forget to give it back. When he opened his phone, looked at me, and said, "You know Kathy, you might want to charge this once in a while!"

It felt like Greg wanted me to find his note, and then he fixed my mistake. He also taught me not to change anything for at least 6 months!

Now It's Your Turn:

List and set up each credit card you own.

Set up your online account by going to each credit card web site. You can do this by searching online the credit card name and going to the login tab.

Go to NEW USER and create a username and password. Be sure to list them here below to have them listed in case of an emergency. By the way, the password you create should not be an easy one. It should have capital letters, small letters, and numbers.

If your card is under two names, and if anything happens to one of you, the survivor should not automatically get rid of the card. This may affect your credit rating, and you actually may need to use the card. Also, if the card is under one name and that person passes away, the surviving spouse or family is not responsible for paying the debt.

You could try to keep the bills all streamlined to one credit card. You may have to pay one large credit card bill. You will have a better idea of the outgoing bills and expenses and accrue points, as well.

A. CREDIT CARDS:

Credit Card Name: _____

Account number: _____

List all who are on this account

1. _____

2. _____

User name: _____

Password: _____

Security questions:

1. Question: _____

Answer: _____

2. Question: _____

Answer: _____

3. Question: _____

Answer: _____

List below any items automatically billed to this card. (You will have to update these when your credit card expires and you receive a new card.)

1. _____

2. _____

3. _____

Credit Card #2

Name: _____

Account number: _____

List all who are on this account

1. _____

2. _____

User name: _____

Password: _____

Security questions:

4. Question: _____

Answer: _____

5. Question: _____

Answer: _____

6. Question: _____

Answer: _____

List below any items automatically billed to this card. (You will have to update these when your credit card expires and you receive a new card.)

1. _____

2. _____

3. _____

Credit Card #3

Name: _____

Account number: _____

List all who are on this account

1. _____

2. _____

User name: _____

Password: _____

Security questions:

7. Question: _____

Answer: _____

8. Question: _____

Answer: _____

9. Question: _____

Answer: _____

List below any items automatically billed to this card. (You will have to update these when your credit card expires and you receive a new card.)

1. _____

2. _____

3. _____

B. AUTOMATIC CREDIT CARD DEBITS:

Update your list so that when your card expires you will have to update all these charged bills on the cards' website. Below are some examples for your reference:

EZ Pass
Oil delivery
Gas
Electric bill
TV and /or Internet
Phone Bill
Gym membership
Mail-order pharmacy
Amazon
iCloud

C. PAYING YOUR BILLS WITH YOUR PHONE:

For convenience, some people use their phones to buy things and have the phone automatically set up to pay for things. These types of payments include ApplePay or Amazon. You are putting your personal information at risk. Record your online personal payments here in this book and disable those payments if you lose your phone. List the online information and bill payments below.

_____

_____

_____

D. CREDIT REPORTS AND IDENTITY THEFT:

What are Equifax, TransUnion, and Experian? These are credit bureaus that post your credit scores. They are important when you apply for a loan. The higher your credit score the easier it will be for the lender to know how reliable you are as a borrower. Credit reports help you understand your credit rating and try to prevent fraud and identity theft. The above three names are the "big" names of a dozen credit bureaus out there. It is a business that collects and sells data regarding one's credit history. These bureaus collect information from credit institutions with which you already have a history with, such as banks, school loans, auto loans, etc.

Now they use this information to create a credit report and credit score.

Therefore, when you want a loan, or to sign up with a utility or even employment, the company can do credit checks on you. You are allowed a free credit report from each of these three companies annually. You can find these free annual reports by filling out a request form on AnnualCreditReport.com. Also, the information in your credit report can be checked for free any time on the site CreditKarma.com. This has two of the three bureaus' informational data on it. These are credit reports from your credit history. If you are looking for your credit score, you may want to view it at myFICO.com. This may cost you a few dollars. Or, you can get a free credit score at CreditKarma.com. Even though this number may not be the exact number as from the three bureaus, it will give you an idea of where your score measures up with others and help you monitor your credit for unusual changes.

These credit bureaus are also important when it comes to fraud and identity theft. A credit freeze blocks lenders from accessing your credit report. The only way they can check your rating is when you lift the freeze, usually with the "PIN" number they send you after you apply. This way, someone else cannot open a credit account in your name. If you are a victim of identity theft, immediately contact each of these three bureaus and tell them to start a fraud alert.

You may or should consider putting a freeze on your credit files, especially if you are not planning any large purchases or loans. A security freeze essentially blocks any potential creditors from being able to apply, pull, or view your credit file. For example, if your credit is frozen, then if someone is trying to steal your identity they can't apply for credit in your name. They may try to apply all they want but they will not succeed in getting new lines of credit in your name.

Again, this book is for you to keep all your updates and important numbers! Please keep this book in a safe place.

Account Freeze:

Equifax:
1-800-685-1111
General # 1-800-797-6801
PO Box 740241 Atlantic Ga. 30374-0241
www.TrustedID.com

Experian:
1-888-397-3742
Experian P.O. Box 9556 Allen, Texas 75013
WWW.EXPERIAN.COM/NEWS/SECURITY-FREEZE.HTML

TransUnion:
800-680-7289
PO Box 2000 Chester, Pa 19022-2000
www.TransUnion/credit-freeze/place-credit-freeze

Each company will give you a confirmation number and a PIN number that you must keep to reverse the freeze.

Equifax Security Freeze:

Username: _____

Password: _____

PIN # _____

Experian Security Freeze:

Username: _____

Password: _____

PIN# _____

TransUnion Security Freeze:

Username: _____

Password: _____

PIN# _____

Greg left a note in his book that he was waiting for me! He was waiting on me to file for my security freeze! "Waiting on you, Kathy!" He had written this in his book on the top of the page!

Spouse's Security Account Freeze (if applicable):

Equifax:

Username: _____

Password: _____

PIN # _____

Spouse's security freeze continued:

Experian:

Username: _____

Password: _____

PIN# _____

TransUnion:

Username: _____

Password: _____

PIN# _____

**Never give out your personal information over the phone or online to anyone you don't know. If the caller is unknown, don't get scammed. DO NOT give out your Social Security number, PIN numbers, date of birth, address, any email passwords and usernames, bank account numbers and credit card numbers to anyone who calls you. If you didn't call them, be very aware.

**It has been made known that you should not use the same login username and passwords for multiple sites. This is even getting more and more important. If you become a victim of a data breach, the username and passwords can be used again when inputted to multiple sites. Be very aware of this. This is a big security risk.

Your Story

This is your time to share your thoughts and stories for your family.

Chapter 3

HOUSEHOLD EXPENSES
AND MAINTENANCE

Now It's Your Turn:

MORTGAGE:

Bank/Mortgage holder: _____

Location: _____

User name: _____

Password: _____

Current payment: _____

Balance: _____

Payment of $ _____

Note if it is automatically deducted from Checking account.

On the (Date): _____

Rate is _____ %

Years _____

Paid off Date: _____

Original Amount: _____

Term Payments: _____

Name on Title: _____

*Reminder: If you finish paying your mortgage, you must remember to pay your taxes, or you will incur a hefty penalty.

Below, write where your title is kept. You will have received a "Letter of Satisfaction" from the mortgage company that should be kept in a safe place. (Safe Deposit Box)

Location of Title: _____

Home Equity Line of Credit (HELOC):

This is referred to as a "second mortgage."

Bank: _____

Line of credit amount: _____

Amount owed: _____

How it is paid: _____

Checking account (Bank name): _____

Automatic debit from: _____

Via mail: _____

REAL ESTATE TAXES:

The bill can be paid in three ways:

1. Through the mail and can be paid by check (no fee)
2. By credit card but may incur a percentage fee
3. Through the mortgage company (check if this is how you have it setup)

BE AWARE! As I mentioned earlier, if the mortgage is paid off, you must continue to pay your taxes, or the fine will be applied, and it is quite a bit of a penalty/fine.

GENERAL TAXES:

These can be paid annually or semi-annually usually. Check with your county of residence.

Months Due: _____

How Paid: _____

Amount: _____

SCHOOL TAXES:

School taxes can be paid annually or semi-annually.

Months Due: _____

How Paid: _____

Amount: _____

VILLAGE TAXES:

If you reside in a place that you pay village taxes, they are usually annually. And they do not come out of the mortgage payments. These are an additional tax.

HOMEOWNER'S INSURANCE:

Provider: _____

Policy Number: _____

Cost: _____

To access online:

1. Go to the web site of the Provider
2. Go to "pay my bill."
3. Enter your email address
4. Create and enter your password
5. Hit "YES" to terms and conditions (you may have to scroll down to find this)

It's OK to press *agree* to terms and conditions. You may want to personalize that it is OK to press *agree* to terms and conditions!

Document your new user name and password on this page.

USERNAME: _____

PASSWORD: _____

If there is no invoice, you are paid up to date. If not, you can continue to pay the way you set it up, either monthly or yearly. If monthly, it may cost you a few dollars extra, but it may be a bit more manageable than a one-time yearly expense. If you choose to pay once a year, add this cost into your budget.

If you press "YES" to have email bills and not paper bills via regular mail, it may also save you some money. However, you MUST check your emails.

UMBRELLA POLICY:

An Umbrella policy is a type of extra insurance that provides liability coverage in addition to your homeowner's policy and /or your auto insurance policy. This may be recommended if you have teenage drivers, or a rental property, or a pool.

If you do carry an Umbrella policy, it is usually on the homeowner's policy but can also be with car insurance policy. It also may just be a separate billing.

If this is included in your overall insurance payment, make sure of this so it does not get dropped.

If you are finding out about this and want this coverage, ask your agent about coverage including the uninsured and underinsured.

Umbrella Policy:

Provider Name: _____

Policy # _____

Cost: _____

Billed Via (auto checking, credit card, mail):_____

The Umbrella policy is usually linked to your homeowner's policy or your auto policy billing.

Electric Bill:

Company name (service provider) _____

Account number: _____

How paid: _____

If paid by credit card, be sure to add this to the list of payments from credit card for renewal. Also, the company may charge you a fee to pay by credit card, and then if you miss a payment, you will incur finance charges.

If you pay with automatic debit, keep this on your bank checking page. It can be debited from the website of the company carrier or your checking account.

FYI

If this bill is an automatic debit from the Electric Co. provider, the bill will debit what you owe or the plan you set up. If this is a debit from your checking account to the provider, you have to set up the amount you want to have paid when due.

TV and/or Internet Provider:

Some service providers are throughout the country, and others are local to your state or region. Some states use Verizon, Optimum, AT&T, Spectrum, etc.

*There are many providers in our USA so please go online to see which one is best for you.

Name of your Provider: _____

Go to the provider's web site

Click on the top tab labeled "Residential":

Login. Create a username and password

Username: _____

Password: _____

You can pay this bill the following ways:

- — Regular mail
- — Online, debited from your checking account
- — Enroll in automatic debit from checking account
- — By credit card. *Make sure your provider does not charge a fee for credit card payment.*

*If you choose credit card payment without a fee, you can accumulate points. And you can lower the number of bills you are paying, but the credit card bill will be much higher.

Oil Delivery:

Current supplier: _____

This bill is paid in the following ways:

— By Mail: Sometimes the bill is left in the mailbox and you can write a check and mail it in. Keep a record of the payments and in your checkbook.
— Pay by automatic credit card (again, make sure there is no extra fee using the credit card.) Update "Credit Card" section of this book for your reference.
— Pay by automatic deductions from your checking account

If opting to pay by automatic deductions, go to your bank's website:

Log in and click the "Bill Pay" tab.

The dropdown menu will show the automatic bills deducted from your checking account.

Add this as an Auto bill pay.

Pay: _____

Gas Bill:

Company Provider: _____

You can opt to pay this bill by the following methods. Mark and update the one you choose.

Credit card: _____

Bank checking account: _____

By mail: _____

Landscape Service:

Company Currently using:_____

Phone # _____

Cost per week for mowing, edging, and beds:

_____

Additional Cost For:

Spring /fall clean up: _____

Fertilization/ weed control: _____

Grub/insect: _____

Sprinkler System Service:

Name: _____

Number: _____

Have sprinklers turned on no later than April 30th.

Close the faucet outside (which was opened for the winter). And open the water in the basement over the sprinkler control box on the ceiling.

For the winter, shut off the sprinkler system and have the pipes blown out by mid to late October. You may need to call for an appointment.

Close the shutoff valve in the basement over the sprinkler control. Open the outside faucet after you close the water off. This should prevent the pipe from freezing with water in the pipe.

How to Enroll in Autopay:

Go to the provider's website.

Log in (Create a username and password)

Username: _____

Password: _____

Select "Bill Pay" tab Select "Edit" or "Change" or "Add" payment method. Document the payment method here.

Payment method: _____

*Remember, if you choose to pay by credit card, go back to the Credit Card section in this book. You can update that section so that when your card expires, you can renew this payment without any issues.

Here is a helpful checklist to make sure you stay on top of your basic home maintenance responsibilities in addition to bills for the home:

- Clean the gutters before the winter
- Check or change the washing machine hoses
- Clean dryer vent
- Have boiler serviced once a year
- Clean fireplace annually
- Vacuum under the refrigerator to clean coils
- Switch batteries to smoke alarms, carbon monoxide alarms and thermostat (usually every November)
- Check and clean air filters for air conditioning units and forced-air heating units
- Have extra keys made and have a set hidden outside
- Turn off water to outside spigots and open faucets outside to prevent freezing of pipes in the winter
- Sprinklers - Air pressure the water out in the fall to prevent freezing of water in the pipes of the sprinkler system, and turn back on in the springtime
- Put storm windows in the late fall and change to screens in the spring
- Take portable air conditioners out in the fall
- Know where the Main Water shut off valve is located in your house! **This is very important.**

*If you have a home with steam heat, you need to remember to drain the boiler water to get the rust out. Do this every other month in the winter.

Your Story

This is your time to share your thoughts and stories for your family.

Chapter 4

CAR INFORMATION

Now It's Your Turn:

A. AUTO INSURANCE

Company: _____

Username: _____

Password: _____

Email: _____

If you have more than one policy (i.e., for each member in your household who is insured) you have to create a username and password for each policy.

If you have drivers who are 18 to 21 in your household, you may want to have them have their own policy to reduce your liability. Doing this may cost a bit more, but the liability to your own personal property and finances would not be at risk. Greg and I had decided to put each of our children on their own policy to limit our liability. You may want to figure the cost versus the risk on paper and with your agent, or with advisement from your accountant or attorney.

Questions sometimes asked for proof of identity:

Father's middle name: _____

Favorite pet: _____

Name of street I grew up on: _____

First car: _____

Where I was born: _____

Add here any other pertinent questions and the answers:

B. Auto Registration

If you own a car, the state requires it to be registered with your state's Department of Motor Vehicles. This process involves providing information about your vehicle and personal information. If you fail to register your vehicle or fail to renew the registration, you could get a ticket, a moving violation, and penalty fees.

Cars need to be registered every two years in NY. You can go to www. DMV.ORG for information about registration renewals in your state of residence.

The state will usually send the reminder by mail. If you do it in person, you will need your driver's license, insurance card, and payment.

Auto registration: _____

Car #1:

Make and Model: _____

Registration due date: _____

Renewal date: _____

Car # 2:

Make and Model: _____

Inspection Due: _____

Registration due date: _____

Renewal Date: _____

The ownership of your cars will have to be changed if one person is no longer driving or alive.

The paper you need to fill out is online under DMV (*in NY - dmv. ny.gov)*

You will need form MV -843

Transfer of Ownership:

You will need a copy of the death certificate, as well as the mileage recorded, the registration, and your driver's license.

You will need to notify your insurance company to remove one name and change the insurance policy to an updated one. You then have to update or change your username and password.

Go back to the Car Insurance section in this book and update this information

- In your state, the form may be different, but the idea is the same.

CAR INSPECTION:

Car inspections are due every year:

Car #1:

Make and Model: _____

Inspection date due: _____

R/N date: _____

Car #2:

Make and Model: _____

Inspection Due: _____

R/N date: _____

In the space below, add any other vehicles:

_____

_____

C. EZ Pass

The Saturday before Greg passed away, he asked me to get his iPad for him so that he can update something in his book. I asked him what he needed, and he was persistent with his pen pointer on his iPad. He searched the EZ Pass website and did all the below steps. He had me write the steps in his book and update it to my credit card number. He already had the pertinent information like the account and password but not my credit card. He said he was worried because he knew I wouldn't know how to do this. I replied saying that I wouldn't even have $10.00 for the bridge.

He turned his head to me and said, "That's what I'm worried about. The bridge is not $10.00!"

We had a good laugh, but I do appreciate him doing this and the memory of this time! He knew my credit card had a few months longer than his before expiring. Then I really would have had a bit of trouble!

Now It's Your Turn:

Go ONLINE to www.e-zpassny.com (or to whichever state you are in)

"My Account tab. "To apply, you will have to download an application or go to the nearest retailer.

Account # _____

Write your account number here so you will always have it.

Password: _____

Last four digits of home phone # _____

Replenish through credit card:

To replenish through credit card:

Name of card: _____

1. Access website
2. On the left click Payment Method
3. Click on EDIT and change credit card information:
4. Update credit card and date of expiration
5. Now go to page 29 in your "Credit Card" section of this book and add EZ pass to auto-pay.
6. Document the amount of money you will be debited from your bank account, checking account, or credit card.

D. Car Maintenance

For the last two years of Greg's life, I was the designated chauffeur. One day while driving Greg, he said to look at this little sticker in the upper left-hand corner to notice when the oil needed to be changed. Funny thing, I had been chauffeuring him, and if Greg wasn't in the car, I never would have looked at it! He had been doing the car maintenance our entire marriage. My daughter married in March of 2018, and in July she called me to say her husband was late from work because he had to get the oil changed for his car. That's when I realized that my son -in -law was on his second oil change! I got into my car and realized I was way overdue! It is important to keep on top of your oil changes to help your car run smoothly.

Here are some tips to help you stay on track:

1. Change the oil every 3,000 to 5,000 miles or every three months. There is a sticker on the upper left windshield with the mileage and the date due estimate. You may want

to keep a record of which vehicle needs an oil change and when.

2. Document any service you have done to each car to keep your records straight.

3. If you don't document the upkeep, keep the receipts of the bills you pay for your car for your records.

4. If you have a battery changed in one car and new tires on another, you should keep this in a log. Also, the warranty for the parts change, so keep track of this as well.

5. Windshield wiper fluid refill:

    a. Open the hood of your car, and you will see a reservoir with a symbol of a windshield with wipers! How clever!

    b. Use a funnel and fill it to the "Fill Line" with windshield wiper fluid.

Car #1

Make and model: _____

Brakes: _____

Tires: _____

Radiator: _____

Battery: _____

Alternator: _____

Other issues:

Oil change: _____

Windshield wipers: _____

Car Maintenance: _____

Car #2

Make and model: _____

Brakes: _____

Tires: _____

Radiator: _____

Battery: _____

Alternator: _____

Other issues:

Oil change: _____

Windshield wipers: _____

E. AAA

AAA ID number: _____

Names of those who are covered: _____

Distance allowed for towing: _____

Phone number: _____

Your Story

This is your time to share your thoughts and stories for your family.

Chapter 5

EMPLOYMENT HISTORY

Now It's Your Turn:

Employment information:

Present company of employment: _____

Past employment companies: _____

_____

Pension: _____

401K: _____

403B: _____

Resume:

Greg had my resume on his computer, and he always would update it if I needed it or if I did change my position or place of employment. As a back up, I recommend you print a copy of your current resume.

Your Story

This is your time to share your thoughts and stories for your family.

Chapter 6

HEALTH INSURANCE

If a life event happens to the family member carrying the health insurance, the surviving spouse will have to address this issue within 60 days.

COBRA (It stands for Consolidated Omnibus Budget Reconciliation Act.)

If you opt for COBRA, even though it is costly, you will not have the deductibles again as if you started in another policy for the present year. You may take this option until you need to renew during the annual enrollment period, which is usually between October-December, but be sure to check since enrollment dates change.

If you do opt to enroll in COBRA, it is good for 36 months in NY. (Find out how long this is available to you in your state) If your loved one was on disability, if they died, if you get divorced or switch to Medicare, you may be eligible for COBRA for 36 months. Otherwise, you may only be eligible for 18 months. Then you will have to enroll in another health plan. Follow up on this information if needed.

Now it's Your Turn:

Name of Health Insurance Company:

_____

Who (in your family) is covered and age:

_____

COBRA:

Company's website _____

Username: _____

Password: _____

ID number (if applicable) _____

Phone number: _____

Reenrollment can be a renewal or a change to add or delete: i.e., optical options, dental options, medical, and prescription coverage.

Reminder: Reenrollment comes every year so keep an eye out for this and watch for the deadline to re-enroll or change benefits.

I recommend that if you do opt for COBRA, even temporarily, have it setup as autopay from your checking account. This is because if you stop paying the premiums, even by missing one payment or late payment, COBRA will end automatically. Make sure you pay the premiums on time!

As a spouse of the employee who died, the spouse can continue coverage for 36 months, in New York. You will have to find out how long the coverage is in your state. This information is very important. If you fail to sign up for COBRA within the time allotted, you will not be able to enroll in this healthcare provider.

My husband had called his company and wrote the phone number that I would need to contact the department for my COBRA health insurance. He had figured out how much the cost would be and recommended to me keep this insurance for now. I truly admire how much courage and strength that must have taken for him.

Affordable Healthcare:

The Affordable Care Act (ACA) added options for Americans. The ACA makes sure that health insurance companies cover all Americans regardless of health status and pre-existing conditions. There are ACA healthcare web sites, which allow you to pick a plan. This being said, if you are not sure, apply for the COBRA to guarantee a health care plan until you can investigate other health care insurers.

There is a wealth of information on the websites if you research how to buy an individual health insurance plan. It takes some time and concentration, but it may offer you options that you are unaware of.

FYI

If you are in the generation where you are now caring for your elderly parents, and one parent passes away, the surviving parent may require COBRA. This is important, especially if the surviving parent is a bit forgetful or unaware of this necessity. The older generation usually had one spouse working, typically the man in that generation. Therefore, if your mom is the surviving spouse, she may need to apply for COBRA. Also, Medicare may not be the primary healthcare insurance carrier.

Medicare

You are eligible for Medicare at age 65. You should apply three months before you turn 65. You do however have a 7-month window (three months before your 65th birthday, the month of your birthday, and three months following your birthday). Medicare will then be your primary health care policy, and you will have to carry a secondary policy to cover what Medicare will not cover.

Also, when you do apply for Medicare, you should have a prescription drug plan. There are options on the Medicare site. Go to Medicare.gov to review some drug plan options. Even if you don't take medications currently, be sure to opt into a plan regardless so that you are not penalized or fined when you decide to enroll in the future. They will have you pay a fine you for each day that you weren't previously covered.

It would be very advantageous to investigate Medicare either through your company, a library or at adult education classes. There is a lot of information and important decisions and choices to make.

Document the Medicare plan you have here:

_____

Your Story

This is your time to share your thoughts and stories for your family.

Chapter 7

RETIREMENT PLANNING

Most companies have a 401K plan or a 403B retirement plan. If you are self-employed, you may have your own financial investment group. Whichever one you have, the following will help you to streamline and keep records for yourself and your family.

If your spouse has left you as the beneficiary to a 401K or a 403B, you should transfer the funds to an existing plan under your name or open a custodial IRA under his/ her name for your benefit. If you take this money out early, you will be responsible to pay a 10% early withdrawal penalty as well as ordinary income taxes. Make sure you have it transferred into an account that is the custodian for the IRA transfer from the 401K or 403B.

Another thing to note is that some of these transfers have a 60-day time period. The company managing your investments may offer advice as to what to do or where to invest the transfer of pension. You can opt to leave it in the company and work with the support of the company's pension managers.

It may be prudent to find a financial advisor or an accountant to help you with these important decisions and to explore options. My husband did corporate taxes for a living, so that's probably why I never gave it a thought. However, due to his illness, Greg had to have someone else do our taxes during the last two years of his life. A great friend recommended us to a reliable, knowledgeable and resourceful CPA. We were very fortunate in that. I truly believe that you could benefit from the knowledge and expertise of a financial advisor.

I also know most people are reluctant to let someone from "the outside" into your personal and financial situation. However, the experts who understand the tax laws and the tax breaks and the knowledge they can offer, especially in trying and emotional times is immeasurable. However, be aware of who you are meeting with and check with friends and family for any referrals. Please make sure that whoever you go to as a financial advisor, that they are fiduciary and that your accountant is versed in estate planning.

I recommend you keep a phone log of all your calls and dates and time to document whom you spoke with and where you left off. You are responsible to ensure that your plan is followed, because mistakes, unfortunately, do happen.

For example, some of my husband's pension was scheduled to be transferred into an account of mine. I sent in pages and pages of documentation they required, the copies of marriage certificate, death certificate and banking routing number and account number. Suffice it to say, the bank said it never was wired, and the company said it was. After four frustrating visits to the bank and about 20 phone calls (all documented) we discovered that the money was wired to the bank all along – but to another bankers' account. It was the bank's error, but this unfortunate back-and-forth transpired for four months! I recommend keeping good documentation of phone calls and whom you spoke to and to follow-up.

Present employer:

Name: _____

Retirement plan (401K, pension, 403B etc.): _____

Previous or past employers and retirement plans, if not already consolidated.

Name of employer: _____

Plan: _____

Name of employer: _____

Plan: _____

Your Story

This is your time to share your thoughts and stories for your family.

Chapter 8

SOCIAL SECURITY

Before I first went to the Social Security office, I had been made aware to bring my husband's death certificate, our marriage license and a voided blank check. They wanted the account number and routing number for the one-time death benefit of $255. After a month, I never received the check. I actually was expecting it in the US mail. I tried to call them and was on hold for a bit when a friend of mine told me to look into our checking account online. Surprise! It was direct deposited. I hadn't even thought about it, but it makes sense. You sometimes have to laugh at the things one spouse does so naturally, and the other has no clue!

There is a one-time death benefit that the surviving spouse is entitled to if he or she was living with the deceased. This one-time payment at present is $255. You will need to call Social Security office 1-800-772-1213 or contact your local Social Security office. It is also very important to know your surviving spousal and/or children's benefits.

The following website is a great help:
https://www.ssa.gov/planners/survivors/ifyou.html

Certain family members may be eligible to receive monthly benefits. There are many situations where the survivors may be eligible for monthly benefits: a widow age 60 or older, a surviving divorced spouse (under certain circumstances), a widow, or widower of any age who is caring for a child who is under the age of 16. The website listed above can provide more details.

If you are a widow or widower of a person who worked long enough under Social Security, you are eligible to receive full benefits at full retirement age for survivors or reduced benefits as early as age 60. There are additional options such as you can apply for retirement or survivors benefits now and switch to the other (higher) benefit at a later date.

If you opt to take one early, it will make sense to investigate and find out which would be most beneficial for you. You can opt for neither if you are still working. If you do take a benefit, meet with the Social Security department to see which figures work out the best. If you decide to take your spouse's benefit, and yours continues to grow, this option may work best. Then you can switch to yours when you are 70, and then that would be the higher amount. This should be calculated by the Social Security office and with you.

Also, put a reminder on your phone or calendar to follow up with Social Security.

Social Security website: WWW.SOCIALSECURITY.GOV

Social Security phone number: 1-(800)-772-1213

Make an appointment for benefits discussion.

Bring ID, Driver's license, passport, marriage license and death certificate, as well as your checkbook. They will use the account number and the routing number to direct deposit your check. Expect a one-time life insurance sum of $255.

Things to consider:

Age:

Age under 60, Over 60, Over 62.

Full retirement age.

Spouses' full retirement age.

Your full retirement age.

Spouse Children under 18.

Over18 -no money due.

On the Social Security paper, it will list some of the companies that you were employed by. This will be helpful to remember if and where you may have had a pension started, but forgot about over the years.

At this time, you may want to consider meeting or discussing your options with a financial advisor.

Your Story

This is your time to share your thoughts and stories for your family.

Chapter 9

ESTATE PLANNING

Learning and investing the time in documenting this information in case of an emergency will help give you peace. I truly believe my husband's life was cut short from me, but I also know by his leaving me this book he has given me peace of mind and the courage and knowledge to keep going.

However, you could make these plans well in advance so that the stress will not scare you or your loved ones.

It would be beneficial for you to look into the following:

1. A **Will** – Having a Will in place is beneficial so that there is no confusion as to who will inherit your assets. This is especially beneficial if you have special wishes, or if you have more than one person to inherit your assets, or if and where you want to be buried, or cremated.
2. A **Health Care Proxy**- This is a document with which a person appoints an agent to legally make health care decisions on behalf of the person when the person is no longer capable of making and executing health care decisions A Health Care Proxy would also be helpful as it could let your wishes be known.

a. I know for a fact that my husband did designate a Health Care Proxy after his diagnosis and after a bit of treatment. It helped his family comprehend his thoughts and wishes. I also know how much harder the elderly seem to deal with the reality of finality. However, all too often you hear stories of family members not speaking or discontent or suspicious of the way things are done. Therefore going to an attorney for a POWER OF ATTORNEY, for a HEALTHCARE PROXY, and a WILL would benefit all.

3. **Power of Attorney** – A Power of Attorney is a written legal document that gives another person the authority to handle your personal business and make decisions if you are incapable of handling your own affairs. This legal document becomes null and void after death. The affairs then become part of the Will, and the Executor of your Will takes over.

4. **A Trust**- For anyone who has significant assets, you may want to put them into a TRUST, so as not to allow young beneficiaries to have access to inheritances at an early age. Or if you have step-children or step-grandchildren, it would behoove you to evaluate and determine how to leave your inheritance. (FYI if you have children, who have stepchildren, and you leave an inheritance to your child, they may get divorced, the spouse can inherit your inheritance if something happens to your child first. Lots to absorb and understand, and to plan!) This book is for basic access to daily living and passcodes as well as Estate direction, but be sure to work with your attorney or advisor for more detailed planning of your affairs.

Attorney's name: _____

Address: _____

Phone number: _____

Accountant's name: _____

Address: _____

Phone number: _____

Your Story

This is your time to share your thoughts and stories for your family.

Chapter 10

FUNERAL ARRANGEMENTS

As overwhelming as it is to actually do, Greg went so far as to pick out his cemetery plot. I wasn't so fond of this idea, but actually when the time came to use it, I truly believe he did me a favor.

We went to the cemetery and took the tour. He actually would lie down on the ground and cross his arms and say, "Not this one!" Then we would drive to another section, and he said, "No. Not this one!" He always did have a sense of humor, and he did this for me. Then we drove to the area where my husband is now and he knew he had found the perfect spot. He is the first plot of the row and said, "No one is going to be trampling on me, and that tree will shade me, and the Blessed Mother is standing over and watching over me."

At the time, he made it as humorous as he could, but it was very difficult for both of us. However, now in retrospect, Greg saved me from having to do a very time-sensitive and stressful task on my own. I now see it as a gift more than I did then and now I am so grateful that Greg did prepare these funeral and burial arrangements with me.

After hearing my story, a dear friend of mine pre-planned these funeral arrangements with her spouse and it saved her the overwhelming burden to have to do this task alone after he passed away. I know that this is very difficult subject to think about, but pre-planning will save you a lot of pain and stress when that time comes.

Now It's Your Turn:

Funeral Arrangements

Cemetery: _____

Cremation: _____

Religious affiliation: _____

Information needed:

Father's name: _____

Place of birth: _____

Birth date: _____

Mother's name: _____

Place of birth: _____

Birth date: _____

Social security number: _____

Military information: _____

Discharge papers: _____

Special organizations: _____

Special Recognition: _____

Charitable organization: _____

Your Story

This is your time to share your thoughts and stories for your family.

Chapter 11

PERSONAL INFORMATION

On May 16, 2018, my husband asked me for his cell phone. Greg always kept his phone next to him but on this day I had moved it to do his morning care. I immediately gave it to him, and he opened his phone. He looked at the face of it and looked at me and said "Kathy, you might want to charge this once in a while, and then he said "I'll sing Happy Birthday to you from heaven." What an amazing man.

My husband passed away on May 17th. My birthday is May 18th. Those beautiful words help me every single day.

Now It's Your Turn:

Computers:

Which computer are you logging into? Some households have more than one, and the user name and password may be locked. Therefore, below is a good place to document the information.

Computer: _____

Login: _____

Username: _____

Password: _____

Phone:

Some phones need a thumbprint but also have a backup 4 or 6 digit password codes. This code is also very important for retrieving information. It also may be a comfort for your loved one to hold onto for a while.

Phone digit pass code: ____-____-____-____-____-____

Email account and social media:

If you and or your spouse have an email account and social media account, it is a safe bet each does not use the login daily. You just open on your device. However in the event of an unexpected occurrence, and to be safe, list your accounts and login information here. I am so grateful that Greg wrote all these passwords and accounts down for me.

Email Account: _____

Login/password: _____

Email Account: _____

Login / password: _____

Social media account name: (E.g. Facebook)

Username: _____

Password: _____

Social Media Account Name (E.g. Twitter):

Username: _____

Password: _____

Your Story

This is your time to share your thoughts and stories for your family.

Chapter 12

LOANS

In this chapter, Greg documented our son's rental for college as well as insurance bills. Greg also figured out the amount I would have to pay to cover our son's student loans. He even figured out the increased rate of tuition and the difference we would owe. He left me a note saying that the university will say it's "this much," but with tuition rate increases, he figured out exactly how much we would owe. He had the month and the amount listed for me for our son's entire senior year. I'm really glad he had figured this out and also left a phone number for me to call if I needed help. (I think it was the bursar's office). Also, my son had an apartment for his junior and senior year at college. Greg figured out the amount he would need to cover the rent. He had the water bill documented as well. He also had the rental insurance company and coverage that we had all listed and what I was to expect to be paying. I am so grateful for this information. He had a page for each of these entities.

Now it's your turn!

Student loans:

Student ID # _____

Email: _____

Password: _____

Bank: _____

Account Number: _____

Date due: _____

Year finished: _____

Rate of interest: _____

Your Story

This is your time to share your thoughts and stories for your family.

Chapter 13

SPECIAL PAPERS AND OTHER PASSWORDS

Please document if you have these papers and where you keep them.

Special Papers	Location
Birth Certificate	
Baptismal Certificate	
Communion/Bar Mitzvah Papers	
Confirmation	
Marriage Certificate	
House Deed	
Car Title	
Survey	
Boat	
Children's Birth Certificates	
Cemetery Deed	
Life Insurance Policy	
Health Insurance	

Auto Insurance	
Tax Return	
Will	
Power of Attorney	
Living Will	
Other Legal Documents	
Deeds	
Stocks	
Jewelry	
Coins	
Cash	
Flash Drive	
Medals	
Other Heirlooms	
Dog Tags	
Professional Licenses	
Professional Affiliations	
Medical Information	
Dr.'s Name	
Dr.'s Number	

Other important points of record:

Passwords and information for the following (add others if needed):

Amazon: _____

Costco: _____

Security Home Camera:

Company: _____

User Name: _____

Password: _____

PayPal/Venmo: _____

EBay: _____

Storage facility if you have one:

Name: _____

Container Number: _____

Keys (where kept): _____

*Some people have many possessions and we would like to pass these on when the time comes. This book is to itemize and keep a record of our personal treasures as a "gift" to pass forward.

Please use this space to add any other items or property you think of:

Your Story

This is your time to share your thoughts and stories for your family.

Extra pages for notes and additions:

Chapter 14

FINAL THOUGHTS FOR MOVING FORWARD

Greg wrote the following letter for our children in October of 2017, and I found it two months after he passed away:

My dear children, what is in store
for your future is a mystery.
Impossible to predict,
but I do know that it will be one of fantastic
opportunities that you should seize and cherish.
Will you fail at an opportunity; maybe,
we all do, but never ever be afraid
to grab that chance.
Life is short my little ones,
love each other check on each other.
Love your Mom!
She's the best mom you could ever have hoped for.
When and if the time comes
love and respect your spouse.
Be kind, gentle even in difficult times
and if you are blessed with children,
I hope they are as wonderful as you
my sweet babies are.

Greg's Gift has helped me tremendously. I refer to this book often. It is also so amazing that people ask me how I knew how or what to do, and I respond with a smile "Oh, it's in the book!"

This book is meant to help each and every one of us because we never know what can happen, nor when. However, being prepared is such a wonderful gift for ourselves and our loved ones.

This book and the topics we addressed is not a death sentence. It is, however, a "Gift" to yourself and your loved ones in the event something should happen to you. Everyone wants to believe that death isn't going to happen to him or her. However, death is a part of life, and if you start now when the time comes, the work will already be done, and the future plans will be made known. It's a gift! Pass it forward!

Thank you for allowing me to share my story and Greg's legacy with you.

Acknowledgments

With my deepest gratitude, I would like to acknowledge my beautiful children, Mary and Jimmy, who have been so strong and compassionate through these tough years. They have supported me every step of the way to help get *Greg's Gift* out there.

I want to thank the O'Driscoll and Golaszewski families for their patience, understanding, support, presence, and love during an emotional time in these new, unchartered waters.

A heartfelt thanks to all of my friends who have supported me emotionally, listened to me for hours and loved me through this journey. I have the most profound gratitude to every one of you. Each of you has given me your unique gift of love and support, and I am forever indebted to you.

I also want to send a special thank you and acknowledgement to Melissa Kuch. She is the most amazing and enthusiastic editor and author. Thanks to Melissa for her encouragement and her guidance to move my book to the final stages of publishing!

And most of all, I thank God for the strength and courage and love He has shown me. Without Him, none of this would have been possible.

About the Author

Kathy Golaszewski was born and raised in New York and is a registered nurse with a specialty in the PACU and critical care. Her world was forever changed when her husband for 36 years, Greg, was diagnosed with Stage 4 Prostate Cancer. Before her husband lost his battle with cancer in 2018, he gifted Kathy with an end-of-life guide to help with the aftermath of his death and ensure a smoother transition with the day-to-day responsibilities. The book not only helped alleviate some of the stress while Kathy was grieving, but it was also a treasured gift. Greg's guide inspired Kathy to write *Greg's Gift* to pass on her husband's gift and legacy while helping others prepare their own plans. This workbook is beautifully interwoven with poignant and, at times, humorous stories of Kathy's life and marriage that will help readers as they fill out their plans and leave a legacy for their loved ones. Kathy currently lives on Long Island and has two beautiful children, a son-in-law, and a grandson. Feel free to visit Kathy on Facebook at <u>Facebook.com/KathyGolaszewski-Author.</u>

Made in the USA
Columbia, SC
01 August 2021